An Introdu... CRYSTAL-REF...

ROGER C CROXSON
BA MPhil

NATURAL SOLUTIONS
WHOLISM
THROUGH

16 Delaware Court
Gunnislake PL18 9BH
1997

The ideas expressed in this book are based on the use of Crystals, Reflexology and Crystal-Reflexology as Complementary Medicines by suitably qualified practitioners. Any readers with a medical condition, physical or mental should consult an appropriate health practitioner.

ISBN 1 901423 01 8

Published by
Natural Solutions Through Wholism
16 Delaware Court Gunnislake PL18 9BH
Tel: 01822 834787 Email: books@wholism.co.uk

CONTENTS

INTRODUCTION

Crystal Reflexology is not magical, but it is powerful, it takes its foundation from Reflexology and Crystal Healing. It is therefore based on the ideas that the body and the workings of the body, emotions and spirit are reflected in the feet; and that all of the body, emotions and spirit vibrate and that the natural vibrations of crystals can resonate within the body to aid healing.

There are many ways of using Crystals combined with Reflexology. Two methods, the first applying a single or a pair of terminated crystals (normally of the quartz family) to the feet, and the second producing layouts on the ground close to the feet, seem to cover most of the processes except for the use of Crystals around the body during a Reflexology session.

Crystal-Reflexology is based on the premise that it is not the healer that heals rather they act as a guide or catalyst for the person to heal themselves. There are of course situations where certain aspects of healing can provide very good results for symptomatic conditions. However this may not be the long term solution which can only come about after a change within the person, probably with several sessions of Complementary Medicine and counselling.

This booklet on Crystal Reflexology has come about from a deep interest in both forms of healing. I find the feet so fascinating in the way that they relay information and I find the power of Crystals to be so strong, beautiful and mystical that a combination seemed the next stage forward.

Although many people have been using Crystals and Reflexology for many years in a variety of forms there did not seem to be very much information available. After considering the problem for some time I realised that the information was available. During several meditation periods I found I had been given the basis for this booklet and assistance in using the two therapies together. This I then supported with study and practice. However, there is still much more work, practice and investigation to be completed.

I am sure that as more work is undertaken that more information will be passed onto us in a variety of ways. This for me is the beginning and the chance to assist the Earth towards a better future, I hope it can be part of your journey as well.

This introduction can only touch the surface, there is still a lot of work to be done to find more efficient methods, more work on Meridians, elements, Chinese Elements and the nervous systems. Many of the processes described appear to be for symptomatic or acute cases, this is only the beginning. For long term and chronic cases the same processes can be used, with different Crystals as the situation changes. It is important to look at the whole person, and aid the whole person to start to heal themselves. I consider that Crystal-Reflexology can act as a catalyst and that it is important to allow the person time for changes to take place.

PERSONAL AND CLIENT PREPARATION

This booklet assumes a basic working knowledge of one or both of the therapies mentioned. The preparation of the client is similar in both, with the taking of medical and personal history, settling them into a safe and comfortable space in the warm and neutral treatment room. Tell them about the treatment, what takes place, that they are in control and to tell you if anything feels unusual or strange.

Even when using Crystals on the feet the process can have a strong physical reaction for the client. It is therefore important to ensure that the client understands Healing Crisis and that you know if they suffer from any illness that may be life threatening such as heart conditions, epilepsy, asthma and diabetes.

If you are not used to working on feet take a few simple precautions, always check for infections, cuts and bruises and cover them and leave alone. Make sure your hands are clean and warm. Always approach the feet with care, the auric layers around the feet can be surprisingly sensitive. If you make contact with the feet try and maintain that contact so that you are not touching, letting go, touching, a process which does not aid client relaxation.

If you have any doubts at all attend a local Reflexology class and read up on the feet. It is important to understand where the various parts of the body are represented on the feet. There are many schools of thought on this so you have to find one that you feel happy with. Again if you are not used to working with Crystals find out more by attending a local class and reading about how to use and look after them. It is important to remember that Crystals are powerful both before and after use. Ensure that the Crystals are cleansed and charged before working with them, and that used Crystals are kept well away from the client. Take care how you wave crystals around, remember that they work at many different levels including all the levels of the Auric Field.

It is important, like all other therapies, that you are also settled, that all your own problems have been left at the door and that you are centred and grounded. Connect your roots to the ground and bring the energy up through your body letting it fountain from the top of your head and return to earth providing you with a curtain of protection; let the white light come into the top of your head and pass through to be grounded when it reaches the earth. Ask your helpers to be with you or say your starting prayer to prepare yourself for work.

Settle your client by leading them through a short clearing meditation or by simple releasing breathing with 3 or 4 deep breaths which they can expel noisily (if they will!). Make sure they are warm as their body temperature will decrease as the treatment continues.

If this is a first treatment don't forget to take the client history before settling them for the treatment. It is always a good idea to allow lots of time for this as many things may well come out that provide clues as to where the real problems may lie. The history should include as much as possible, but only that which is relevant. You can always follow a particular path if necessary. Don't forget to assure clients about the confidentiality of the treatment session.

A BRIEF LOOK AT THE FOOT

As has been stated, in Reflexology the whole body is mirrored in the feet, the left hand half of the body in the left foot and the right hand side of the body in the right foot. In conventional Reflexology the Big toe represents the Head and the Heel the Pelvic region, with the arms and legs at the outside of the foot.

There are many forms of Reflexology in use in the West, there are many very different types used in other cultures and these are now beginning to be recognised. With Crystal-Reflexology the classical pattern of the body on the foot is used as a basis, to this can be added the

Chakra-Endocrine Systems and the Meridians.

Although a majority of the work is with Crystals close to the feet there are still times when it is helpful to use thumb or finger pressure on the feet as either part of the treatment or as a means of identifying the correct place to direct the energy of the Crystal. Do not be afraid to make contact with the feet.

With conventional Reflexology the places that need work can often be identified in one of three ways:

1. To feel a very small indentation or small lump with an indentation rather like a very small volcano. This can indicate that you are spot on the place you intend to work.

2. Granular crystals that creak and crunch when gently pressed, these are often a sign of blockage and can be removed with appropriate pressure.

3. A scream or jump by the client indicating that you have gone to the source of the blockage.

All of these can help find where the crystal work should take place. It is important that if you have not worked with these processes before to obtain expert guidance. When used for identifying places to put or aim Crystals the areas under consideration should be treated very gently and with the utmost consideration. If you find a point then stop work on it, do not press for any longer than needed for identification.

However, it can be important to maintain contact with the feet whilst using Crystals, and when ever possible keep part of at least one hand touching the foot that is being worked on. Also before using the Crystals it is possible to use relaxing techniques on the feet to encourage the client to leave behind the stresses and strains of the day. And at the end of the treatment a gentle stroking massage can be very healing as well as bring the clients attention back to their body, ready to carry on.

The opening relaxation massage can also assist in identifying areas of need. This is by the feel of the feet and the reactions of the client. It is important to always keep an eye on the client, both on their feet, looking out for changes, twitches, temperature and colour; and the rest of the body, including the face.

The basic strokes for the opening massage are:

1. Gently but assuredly hold both feet with the thumb on the bottom of the feet, just below the ball of the foot. Gently press the Solar Plexus

point of both feet simultaneously, holding for a few seconds, repeat three times. Be considerate when first making contact with the feet as you are passing through the Auric Field which can be very sensitive on the feet.

2. With both hands in a circular manner work up and down the sides of one foot, the gentle pressure balancing the pressure of the other hand. Work up and down the foot twice. Then do the same on the other foot. Always work with alternating feet, don't finish one foot with everything before moving onto the next.

3. On the top of one foot with both hands gently stroke down from toes to ankle using the tips of the fingers. Repeat several times covering all of the top and well into the sides of the foot. Repeat on the second foot.

4. Support the top of the foot with one hand and with the fist (Knuckle to first joint) of the other stroke down the foot in a series of four runs covering all of the foot. Repeat on second foot.

5. Cover both sides of the ankle with the palms of your hands and gently rotate.

At the end of the whole session a gentle stroking massage from the lower leg to the toes using a suitable essential oil can add a little extra to the treatment.

Remember to rinse your hands before and after each treatment, this is for two reason - physical and psychic. It removes physical impurities, such as bacteria and fungi spores; and it helps remove unwanted negative energy that can build up on the hands which can reduce the effectiveness of the practitioner.

A BRIEF LOOK AT CRYSTAL HEALING

Crystal Healing is a very powerful tool in the process of helping a person help themselves on the road to change, whether that be physical, mental, emotional or spiritual. It is important to recognise that Crystals are not inert pieces of rock, they need to be chosen and cared for with love and attention. They are not to be waved around in a haphazard manner, nor are they to be used without consideration for the client and intent on your behalf.

In the initial stages of Crystal-Reflexology it is possible to work with a small tool kit. Most important are a pair of Clear Quartz Points about 11/2 to 2 inches long, a short Crystal Wand and a set of Chakra Crystals in the form of tumbled stones (Amethyst, Sodalite, Blue Lace Agate, Rose Quartz, Citrine, Carnelian and Smoky Quartz). Others can be substituted for these. It may also be helpful to have Amethyst and Citrine points. A Double Terminated Clear Quartz Crystal can also be useful.

In order to obtain these stones you have to choose them, there are various ways of doing this including: looking, feeling and dowsing. Again follow guidance in other publications or attend a course.

Having chosen your Crystals it is really important to cleanse and charge them. Again there are several ways this can be done. Cleansing is thought to remove the positive ions from the stone and replace them with negative ions, this means any negativity is removed and the stones are provided with a positive and healing energy similar to the energy you get from standing near a waterfall. In general all Quartz based Crystals can with-stand being immerse in salt water. Unless they have been particularly badly looked after, 24 hours in a salt water solution should be enough. Then take them out and rinse them in clean water. If possible use natural spring water but if necessary tap water will work. Some Crystals do not appreciate water or salt water so be careful, if in doubt don't leave Crystals in water.

Another way is to hold them under running water but beware as they do have a tendency to run away. One method that works with all types of Crystals is Smudging. Smudging, an evocative word, is a lovely process. It is the burning of herbs, and once more the burning herbs are thought to affect the ion balance of their surroundings. The most common herbs to use are Sage, Cedar and Sweetgrass which are available in packets as a mix or in a bundle. There are other combinations including Mugwort, Lady's Bed Straw and Lavender. The herbs are lit and the Crystals are held in the smoke. It may be necessary to waft the herbs to keep them smouldering and smoking, a feather works very well, or even a wing or part of a wing from a bird of prey, (they are protected birds so only buy their feathers from a reputable dealer or find your own from a road kill and return a little token to the Earth in exchange for your gift).

Another method that can be used is that of blowing on the Crystal with the strong intent of cleansing it.

Having cleansed the Crystal the next stage is to charge it. The easiest way to do this is to place the Crystal on a sunny widow sill or in a sunny spot in the garden. Leave it there for a day or if you prefer a night in the light of the moon. Other natural energies can be utilised such as thunderstorms and fast running water. Remember that the Crystal will be energised with the energy it is subjected to.

Having energised your Crystals get to know them. This is very important so that you understand the energies imparted by the Crystal to the client. Place the Crystal in your receiving hand which in general for right handed people is the left hand and for left handed people the right hand. Hold the Crystal and bring your hand up to your heart. You can bring your other hand up to cover the other. Relax and just let the feelings from the stone enter your mind. You can ask it "what is its purpose in being with you, how can it help in your work"? Let the answer come, believe in what you see, hear or intuit.

The energies of Terminated Crystals come from three places, each with a different energy: the point, the strongest and most directed energy; the triangle or other multisided part that helps form the point and the side or blade of the Crystal. Experience these by holding the Crystal in your sending hand and moving the Crystal over your open receiving palm at different angles.

Now that you have experienced the energies of Crystals keep practising. It is now time to look at the different ways in which Crystals can be added to Reflexology.

PROTOCOL

The processes that follow are powerful and need to be treated with care. The time taken to undertake the work is often much shorter than in conventional therapies. Do not keep at it just because the client expects that the session should last a specific period. If necessary or as part of the treatment let the client relax, or talk about one of their problems.

In all cases limit the work to two direct treatments per session plus one indirect. Direct is the specific work on a particular reflex, indirect is an Auric Massage or Chakra layout. If the indirect treatment is last and of a relaxing general nature then just let the client go with it giving time for the healing process to take hold. Remember that relaxation is the first part of the healing process. You can give them a pair of Rose Quartz or Aventurine Crystals to hold. Make sure they are warm and comfortable, possibly with a roll under the knees and let them give themselves that rare commodity of space.

Give a short period of time between any two direct treatments to allow for the changes in energy to take place. If the client appears safe and comfortable leave the room for a few minutes but explain this at the beginning of the session so they do not feel abandoned.

CRYSTAL-REFLEXOLOGY

The way in which Crystals can be used on the feet falls into two main categories: with the client lying down or with the client sitting with their feet on the ground. These two methods can be divided up as follows:

1. Bottom of Feet available

2. Feet on the ground

It is not intended to look at these processes in great depth within this introductory booklet, however the basic outline of the basic forms is given along with brief descriptions of some of the systems they can be applied to. Many problems are caused by energy blockages, this is applied in a rather symptomatic manner but in the initial stages the client does want to feel better as soon as possible. The underlying cause of the problem can be dealt with as in a series of treatments. Crystal-Reflexology is wholistic, it looks at the whole person but sometimes simple treatments can be effective. It is, however, important to give relief if possible in the short term and explain that further work may be required to look at the real cause of the symptom.

Although all references are to Foot Reflexology most of the systems described can be applied to the hands.

THE LINKING APPROACH

This is based on Linking or Precision Reflexology. A gentle touch method which is very effective and which lends it self to the use of Crystals. It appears to work by short circuiting and or connecting various energy channels in the body. It is a very effective method of calming and relaxing clients and can be used after the Solar Plexus massage. Using Crystals the energy is taken down through the spine reflex to the base. From the Pituitary Gland reflex to the Base Chakra Reflex. See Diagram 1.

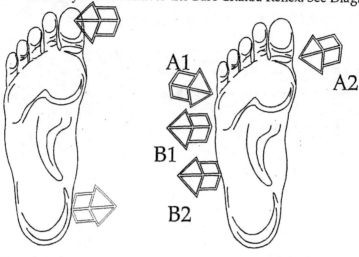

DIAGRAM 1
RELAXATION LINK
WITH CRYSTALS

DIAGRAM 2 REMOVING A
BLOCKAGE WITH A
PAIR OF CRYSTALS

It also works well when there seems to be physical problems such as Bladder Control and pain in shoulders and wrists. For these and other problems the first decision to be made is what is the direction of the flow of energy. In general at this stage we will assume that the energy should be flowing from head to hand or head to toe. The next stage is to work on the problem described by the client.

For example assume that there is pain in the shoulder joint: first place Crystal A slightly above the shoulder reflex on the path to the head with the point towards the foot, next place Crystal B with its base on the foot just below the shoulder reflex. Before placing the Crystals it is possible to gently palpitate the appropriate area to feel the area of concern, or to feel around the appropriate reflex with either the second finger or the palm of your sensing hand to feel the energy around the foot and ascertain where to place the Crystals. See Diagram 2.

Hold the Crystals until you feel they should be moved, which may not be very long. These are the same Crystals that are used on the body, their energy is the same but the size of the reflex is much smaller than the body component. Often there will be some kind of movement either of the foot or in the foot indicating that there has been a change in the energy pattern. This can be a twitch, muscle spasm or a jump. It is therefore important to keep your eyes open even though it is tempting to close them as the meditative state takes over. Then move both Crystals away from the starting positions along their respective paths of energy, in this case a path back to the Spine Reflex and down the Arm Reflex, and hold them again until they are ready to move. Keep moving them until they reach the Spine Reflex and the Hand Reflex. Again there may be a response and an indication that a change in energy has occurred at the physical level, although it may very slight. The number of moves is dependent on how many you feel is necessary, two may be enough, it depends how the energy moves so monitor the energy floor each time the Crystals are moved.

Use the hands to check on the flow of energy, remember the client may have an immediate response or it may take a little while to go from the reflex to the body, and is dependent on the particular problem. The process is then finished and can be followed by an auric massage with a lump of Rose Quartz or other suitable stone, work on another area or a gentle foot massage.

USING A PAIR OF CRYSTALS

Within today's society, the body picks up a lot of negative, unpleasant energy which either reduces the efficiency of the body or in extreme cases manifests as illness or disease. By removing this negative energy and replacing it with positive, caring energy the client can continue refreshed and invigorated. The areas that can be affected are the Chakras and glands such as the Adrenals.

This process uses the classic system of removing negative energy with one hand, disposing it to Earth with the other and reversing the process to energise the affected part bringing in White Light. Again it is very important that you do not drain your own energy so bring up Earth energy and bring down star energy, when this loop is working add a third dimension: hold a pair of quartz terminated Crystals in your hands with the point towards hand in the receiving hand and the point away in the sending hand. Feel the flow of energy up the arm , around the base of the neck and down the other arm and out of the Crystal.

These areas of negative energy can be felt or dowsed for either on the person or on the feet. First with the receiving hand hold the base of the Crystal over the area and with the sending Crystal point to earth and turn in an anticlockwise direction asking that the negative energy be taken and transmuted into good energy. When you feel that this has taken place shake both hands and Crystals and reverse the hands so that the sending Crystal is pointing towards the foot and the sending hand is held out to receive energy. Gently spiral the sending Crystal in a clockwise direction moving it in and out as you feel is appropriate until you consider the area being worked upon is sufficiently energised. This can then be checked by talking to the client and/or using a pendulum or by feeling with the hand.

USING SINGLE CRYSTAL POINTS

Many of the approaches to Crystal-Reflexology are very similar, like the approaches to Crystal Healing, but they do have different effects and the decision which one to use does depend on the needs of the client and the intuition of the practitioner.

Circling is similar to the removing and sending energy but is undertaken with only one Crystal. Again negative energy is removed and positive energy is given back. This single Crystal process is a useful one for working on very specific areas and for the Chakras. To remove energy the Crystal is rotated anti-clockwise, normally held in your dominant hand. To give energy the Crystals are rotated clockwise. The circling can be spiral in nature, an important aspect, as with all of this work, is your intent. Starting with small circles draw out to larger circles and move upward. As always it is important to concentrate on what is happening, keep your mind on the process of removing negative energy. As you go upward you may feel the negative energy being removed from the auric layers, the blueprint of the physical body and related to the Chakras. The energy pulled out by the Crystal can be shaken to the earth with the mental or verbal intent asking the earth to take the energy and transmute it for the good of all. You may want to repeat this process several times.

Having cleared the negative energy out it is important to replace it with positive energy. This is the reverse process. Again holding the Crystal in your dominant hand rotate it clockwise. Start from above in wide circles and work down decreasing the size of the circle until you reach a point close to the foot. This time you may feel the Crystal get hard to turn indicating that either the area has not been cleared sufficiently or that the place is full of the infused energy. Always follow your instinct and stop rather than carrying on regardless.

At the end check the foot and its energies by gentle touch, pendulum or scanning, and use an Auric Massage.

THE CHAKRA AND ENDOCRINE SYSTEMS

The Chakras are the main energy centres of the body, they have many connections and relationships and can act as a guide to where a problem may exist and to the overall health of an individual. They work at several different layers, from the physical up through the auric layers. They can be assessed by scanning or using a pendulum on the body or the feet.

The circling system works well when the Chakras need toning up. It can help remove some of the debris and replace it with energy to help the Chakra start to return to its most effective state. There are several ways of doing this, the two chosen here are working on the Chakra Reflex points directly on the feet and working on the Endocrine-Gland-Reflexes associated with each Chakra. The reason for this are many. One of the massages that can be included in an ordinary Reflexology treatment is spending time following through the basic Endocrine glands, the Pineal, Pituitary, Thyroid, Thymus, Pancreas, Adrenals and Gonads. This is both to encourage balance and for them to work efficiently and where appropriate to connect to each other, in particular the Pituitary to the others. In Crystal Healing a lot of work is based around the Chakras on the body so this again brings the two therapies together.

Each Chakra has a related Endocrine Gland and it is possible to work on the Chakras via their appropriate Gland. The following table provides one example of the relationships, there are others and it may be that there is a difference between the sexes, which one you use is entirely up to you.

Table 1 Chakra - Gland relationship

Chakra	Gland
Crown	Pituitary
Brow	Pineal
Throat	Thyroid
Heart	Thymus
Solar Plexus	Pancreas
Sacral	Gonads
Base	Adrenals

The first Chakra energy process is working on the Chakra Reflexes. It is possible to work from the top, the Crown, to the Base or from base to Crown depending which way the energy of the person needs to be moved which may be identifiable from the general appearance and attitudes. However, a third method which seems to be very balancing, is to start at the mid-point, the Heart Chakra and move down to the Solar Plexus, then up to the Throat, then down to the Sacral, up to the Brow, down to the Base and finally up to the Crown. This brings together the Lower Chakra energies and the Upper Chakra energies, the Earth energies meeting the Spiritual energies in a balanced manner.

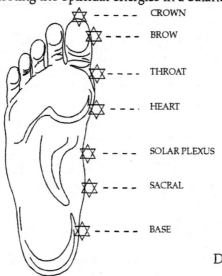

CROWN
BROW
THROAT
HEART
SOLAR PLEXUS
SACRAL
BASE

DIAGRAM 3

To make the best use of this Chakra Balance it is useful to have a Double Terminated Clear Quartz Crystal. This is used to balance the Chakra Reflexes after working on each Chakra on both feet. Hold the Double terminated Crystal between the point at the level of the Chakra for a few moments.

The positions of the Chakras on the feet are shown in Diagram 3. It is possible to feel for them. The place of the Chakra normally has an indentation on the spine reflex. Starting with the Heart Chakra on the right foot use the Clear Quartz Point in an anti-clockwise direction until you feel it has finished its job. Change to the left foot Heart Chakra and repeat. Then return to the right foot Heart Chakra and use the clockwise motion and when ready return to the left foot Heart Chakra and repeat the clockwise movement. When you feel that both feet have been cleared and charged place the double terminated Clear Quartz Crystal between the left & right Heart Chakras for a short time. This helps the body and auric fields of the two feet become balanced.

This procedure is followed next for the Solar Plexus Chakra Reflex, then the Throat, Sacral, Brow, Base and finally the Crown Chakra Reflex. Each Chakra Reflex may require more or less work than the one before. If the client is a very heady person it may be better to work in the following order - Heart, Throat, Solar Plexus, Brow, Sacral, Crown and Base. The effect can be very soothing and relaxing for the client as well as energising to their subtle system.

The second way of using the Chakra System is on the related Endocrine Reflexes as described above. For this one start at the top and work down. As you work keep in mind the relationship between the Chakra and the Gland, the function of the Chakra and the Function of the Gland, not its full chemical function but its overall function. Where you feel there is extra strain spend longer on the Reflex. If necessary the unwinding followed by the winding can be repeated on the same Reflex point when you feel that the inward energy is not working properly. Do not repeat more than twice. The pattern and placing are shown in Diagram 4.

Care must be taken not to over stimulate any of the Glands as this will cause greater imbalance that before. For a Gland like the Adrenal which is under constant aggravation be very gentle and consider how to ease the stress placed on it and bring a positive energy in to it to enable it to function in a beneficial way.

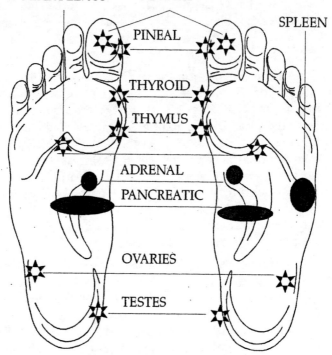

SOLAR PLEXUS   PITUITARY

SPLEEN

PINEAL

THYROID

THYMUS

ADRENAL

PANCREATIC

OVARIES

TESTES

DIAGRAM 4   ENDOCRINE & OTHER
CHAKRA RELATED GLANDS

USING STONES ON THE CHAKRAS

Another way of working on the Chakra Reflexes is to use a relevant stone
over the Chakra reflex. Here the Chakra is massaged with the relevant
Crystal.   Again in a specified order, preferably starting at the Heart
Chakra. This will provide the correct type of energy to the Chakra rather
than the cover all Clear Quartz. There is more about this under Chakra
Layout for feet on the ground. The Crystal is moved in the same way as
above, in a clockwise circle. One Clear Quartz Crystal could be used for
all of the points to remove negative energy, and a different stone could

be used for energising each of the points.

WANDS

Wands are normally added to a Crystal collection as the worker builds their tool box. They are not the Sooty Magic Wands but pieces of Crystal that have been shaped, so that they have a termination at one end and a round dome at the other. They fit into your hand and feel wonderful. They also come in a variety of different Crystals. This can mean that there will be a terminated wand from a Crystal type not normally associated with terminated stones. This means that the energies of other Crystals can be applied to the reflex points on the feet or as an Auric Massage.

When to use Wands? The main time is when there is a specific need. The Clear Quartz provides good energising properties but you may feel that there is a need for energy or love and want to use a Citrine or Rose Quartz Wand. This may be applied to a Chakra Reflex or a specific Reflex where there is a problem. The Wand would normally be used after the area has been cleared by either a single point or by a Clear Quartz Wand. The Wand is used either by pointing directly or by circular motion.

Wands have an added advantage over other terminated Crystals. They have very well defined faces and sides. They can be used to either infuse a more gentle energy by using the triangular faces or for a massage over the feet by using the sides or blades of the Wand. This may be useful at the end of a treatment session.

Always remember that a Wand is a powerful instrument and should not be left lying beside the client, it should be moved away from them and you. This applies to all Crystals used, partly so they do not work for longer than required and partly so the negative energies do not go back to the client.

MERIDIANS

Meridians have come to us like many other great Complementary Medicine tools through time and from the East. Well documented in early Chinese literature they have now been proved to exist. Like our circulatory and lymphatic systems the Meridian System goes around the body. Each pair of Meridians takes a specific name, normally of the major organ it is related to, it also relates to many other parts of the body through which it passes. In general there is one of each type of Meridian for each side of the body so they fit into the bi-polarity of Reflexology. The principles behind the Meridians and the basis of the element system used is beyond this booklet.

From the feet's view point there are at least three ways of working on the Meridians:

1. Using the end points of those Meridians that terminate in the foot Diagram 5.

2. Using the map of Meridians shown in Diagram 6, this is based on the work of Masunaga and the Zen Meridians

3. Taking the mirror theory of Reflexology and applying it to Meridians thus recreating the Meridians on the feet and hands. There is a different set of Meridians for the hands and feet.

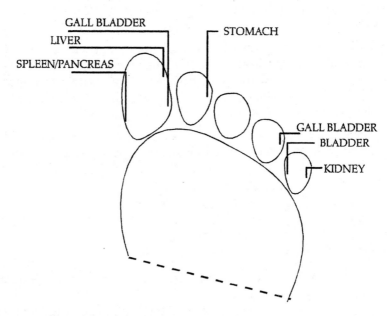

DIAGRAM 5
MERIDIAN END POINTS
ON THE FOOT

The Meridians can be used for a variety of problems with one or two Crystal points or they can be traced through the body to provide a means of energising or calming the whole Meridian.

There are lots of excellent books on the Meridians, they are often explained in books on Shiatsu and Acupuncture.

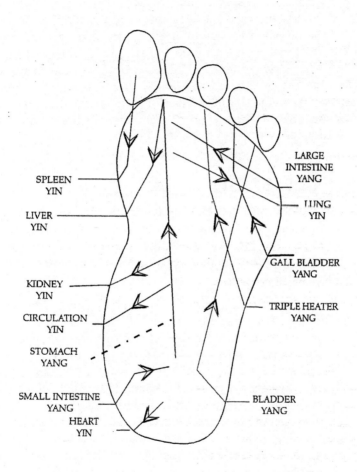

DIAGRAM 6
MERIDIANS ON THE FOOT BASED ON THE ZEN
PATTERN

Two approaches that can be applied are the end of meridians on the feet, and the pattern in Diagram 6. The first activates the Meridian and can be used for problems that directly relate to organs and parts of the body that the meridian passes through where there appears to be an energy blockage. The process is to use a wand or terminated Crystal to first clear and then energise the meridian end point.

The second looks at a Meridian pattern based on the Zen approach and developed by Masunaga. On Diagram 6 the direction of flow of the energy of the meridian is shown. To clear any blockages the meridian pattern on the foot can be energised by using a pair of Crystals with the flow in the appropriate direction. It is also possible to use a single point, wand or other Crystal to trace the Meridian pattern feeling for blockages and removing them as the Crystal moves along the line. It is recommended that a knowledge of meridians is gained before trying these healing methods.

AURIC MASSAGE

A favourite method of either clearing the gunk from around a client or for providing an all over feeling of well being from a given Crystal such as Rose Quartz. The Massage uses either the side blade of a wand or terminated Crystal, or a lump or massive, again for instance Rose Quartz.

There are two basic massages:

1. To remove layers of debris from the Auric Field This can be felt when assessing the client as an auric fog, a treacle like substance or tingly layer. The Crystal is smoothed over the foot an inch or so away, depending on where the layer is felt. Whatever is removed must be sent to earth for transformation to a neutral or beneficial energy, not left in the air. To remove the negative energy from the Crystal a sharp shake towards earth with an intent for the energy to be dealt with in a positive way works well. The direction of the massage is dependent on the situation, but from the top to the bottom of the feet in parallel lines is effective. It is also following the levels of density from lighter to heavier and may avoid cross contamination.

2. To place the energy of a given Crystal into the Auric Field.

This is achieved by gently stoking the blade of a Crystal through the aura of the foot. Again in downward strokes or in a polishing pattern. It is important to remember what your intent is and where you are working. The foot is very sensitive at all levels.

An Auric Massage can be used independently or can be very nice in the opening and closing stages of a normal Reflexology treatment.

CRYSTAL WORK DURING A REFLEXOLOGY TREATMENT

This seems to be an excellent combination and favoured by many practitioners. The choice is up to you, a good knowledge of Crystals is needed along with a good level of sensitivity as there are two levels of help being applied to the client at once. The more basic processes are probably better, such as placing a Rose Quartz in the hands or on the heart Chakra. Grid layouts around the couch using Clear Quartz, Amethyst or Rose Quartz work well particularly where there is a lot of emotional activity.

Grounding stones at the feet may also feel appropriate where the client is absorbed within their head, or is a "space case". In cases of injury Hematite can be very beneficial and for those going through change or where the Reflexology is bringing about change Amethyst can help. A useful guide is *Crystals and Gemstones* by Sue Phillips.

Crystals can also be used for a particular problem during a normal treatment or for subtle work at the end of the physical treatment, for instance as a massage or for working through the Chakras. It is important to inform the client that you may do this as you may not be in physical contact with the client for some parts of the Crystal work, a normal signal that you have finished the treatment session.

USING CREATED COLOUR

In extreme acute cases it may help to throw lots of processes at the problem. The use of colour works well with Crystals. Applying the appropriate colour and the locking complementary colour to a particular spot followed by the use an appropriate Crystal can give better results than when each treatment is used separately. For instance to try and energise an area apply orange followed by blue, then use a Citrine wand to circle energy into the same point.

An alternative is to use the Crystal first and extract negative energy, then apply the colours and finish off by using the Crystal to apply further energy. After this type of intense treatment it is important to leave several days before the next treatment to allow the body to work on itself. It is important to give further treatments before the condition has a chance to reappear. These further treatments may help remove the problem for longer periods or altogether as they allow time to investigate the real cause.

All of these processes have been with access to the bottom of the feet, the next section deals with the feet on the floor.

FEET ON THE GROUND: INTRODUCTION

The benefit of feet on the ground is the possibility of creating a proper layout of Crystals on or around the feet. They can be left there until the time is right for them to be removed. It also removes the influence of the practitioner who can stand back and observe, and maybe see things not visible from the normal close work position. It is also a non invasive treatment for those who find it hard to lie down or who do not want their feet touched. The principles of the process remain the same but a different approach is used, the main approaches are the Crystal Grid, Crystal and Gem Layouts, and Chakra layouts.

Crystal Grids are a means of removing and applying energy to a person, and Crystal Layouts provide the aura and body with a series of energies to help return the body to some form of balance. They also allow space for the client to express themselves or simply to relax, both part of the healing process.

CRYSTAL GRIDS

Crystal Grids are a very powerful way of setting up patterns of energy. The Crystals are placed in predetermined patterns which increase the effect of the individual Crystals, a synergistic process. The Crystal grid works at energy levels higher than the physical, but the effect on the higher levels will probably drop down to the physical level, improving all other aspects of the individual on its way through. Because this is a synergistic process the types of Crystals used and their alignment is very important. Some of the books that describe grid work on the body use hundreds of crystals, for this to work the Crystals have to be in balance with each other. These days it is difficult to find a pair or even six Crystals that are in balance. It is possible to use pairs where larger sets are not available. To find a set or pair choose by shape, size and a lot of intuition, feel them, experience their energy and dynamics.

It is possible to use lumps of Crystals when using forms such as Rose Quartz but the effect will not be as strong, but then Rose Quartz is a gentle healer. The quartz Crystals are the best for the basic grid systems.

Crystal grids can be used for clearing and for infusion. Some authorities seem to only use them for the infusion of energy, connecting to the Universal Energy Field. There are many layouts but at this stage it is better to keep to the simple ones, if only to keep the number of Crystals required to a sensible level.

The basic layout is the Star of David, a very old symbol adopted by various groups as their symbol. However it is used in Sacred Geometry and Crystal work as it represents a balance. It can be constructed from two triangles, the inverted triangle represents the perfection of Spirit moving towards matter and the upright triangle represents the growth of matter towards Spirit. The balance and equilibrium is represented by the interlocking of these two triangles. When superimposed over the Chakra system the mid point, the intersection, is at the Heart Chakra.

It is important when using grids that the correct geometric pattern is created. If necessary a plan can be place on the ground and the feet placed on the plan. This will ensure the correct angles and directions are obtained. See Diagram 7.

It is possible to clear and infuse at the same time. This can be achieved by using Amethyst and Clear Quartz Crystals. A pair of Crystals is placed at each point, a Clear Quartz pointing towards the feet to infuse and an Amethyst, pointing out, to clear. It is possible to use two Clear Quartz, but Amethyst is good at transmuting negative energies drawn out so that they re-enter the atmosphere in a non-harmful state.

If required the grid process can be used as a self healing process as there is no need for third party interaction. Sit in a chair, place a plan on the floor, add the Crystals and place feet in the middle. Relax and feel the benefit gained.

As stated before there are many other forms of grid work, some of which can be applied to the feet. Use all of them with care.

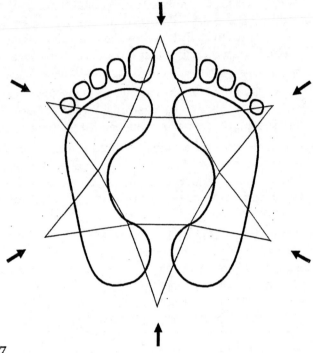

Diagram 7

CRYSTAL & GEMSTONE LAYOUTS

This could be the largest section in the booklet, however, all of the information required is in other publications. At this stage there are two types of layout to consider, the balancing layout, which uses the Chakras as key points and the healing layout which may use the same points together with other Reflex Points.

One question is where to place the stones, it is possible to place stones on the feet, but they tend to fall off. It is better to place stones on the ground, between and around the outside of the feet. For Chakra work the stones are placed between the two feet, which need to be fairly close together, for other work, for instance on the shoulder, the stones can be placed close to the Reflex point under consideration.

To undertake a Foot Crystal Healing it is important to find out the state of body through the feet. The first stage is to obtain information from the client, the normal questions on health and expectations, the safety questions - heart, epilepsy, diabetes etc.. Then an energetic reading is needed, some people can 'see' what the situation is, others can feel and many more can use a pendulum. Keep records as you work so you can monitor how the treatment is going. Having obtained information a set of Crystals needs to chosen, this requires experience and use of Crystals. It is not really a good idea to use a book as the source of information, there are many ones available and some say the same things and some don't. What is important is how a Crystal feels to you. The intuition is very important in Crystal healing.

Having said that, there are some very good basic balancing layouts. Refer to the section on Chakras for the basic position of the stones. The stones used in this layout are all tumbled, no points.

Table 2 A basic layout.

| Crown - Amethyst |
| Brow - Sodalite |
| Throat - Blue Lace Agate |
| Heart - Rose Quartz |
| Solar Plexus - Citrine |
| Sacral - Carnelian |
| Base - Smoky Quartz |

This should be left in place for between five and ten minutes depending on how you feel the treatment is progressing. After which time the stones should be removed from the area of the client and a gentle Crystal massage can be given over the top of the feet, from leg to toes. The client should then be left for a few minutes to enable the treatment to gain a hold within the persons system.

If there are other areas that need attention these can be looked at during the treatment by the application of applicable stones.

ENDWORD or THE BEGINNING

This has been a very quick journey through Crystal-Reflexology, which I trust will encourage you to find out more both from within and without. I hope that a more advanced book will be published at some point. There is more work needed to see what the long term benefits are and how the Crystals interact with the Reflexology. Hopefully from this start many new trees will grow. Many Reflexologists are now learning about Crystals with an almost innate need to put the two therapies together. Lets hope it will gain the recognition that it rightly deserves.

If you require further information about Crystal Reflexology or Courses contact: Roger Croxson The School of Crystal Reflexology Tel: 01822 834787 EMail: info@crystal-reflexology.co.uk